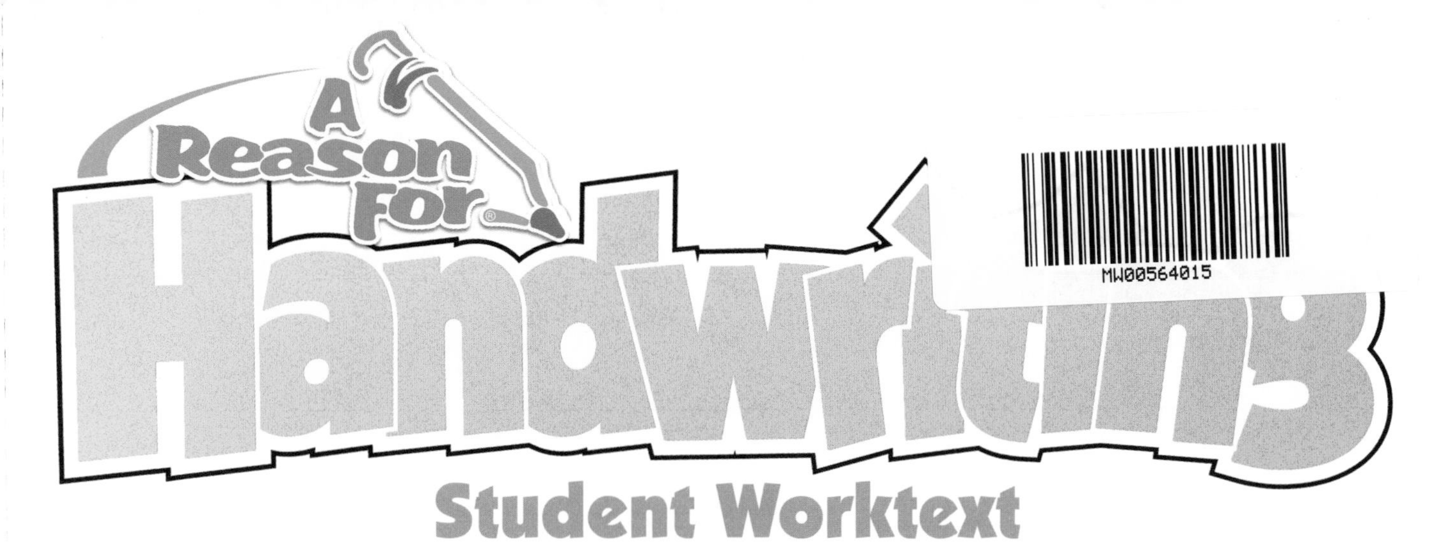

Student Worktext

Manuscript A

EAN#: 978-0-936785-38-7
ISBN#: 0-936785-38-1
TL#: HWSWTA2019WC
2017 Edition

Published by Concerned Communications, LLC
P.O. Box 1000 • Siloam Springs, AR 72761

Authors **Carol Ann Retzer**
Eva Hoshino
Proofreaders **Daniel Swatsenberg**
Marcie Smith
Layout **Mark Decker**
Melissa Habermas
Illustrations **Rob Harrell**
Colorists **Josh & Aimee Ray**

Scripture translation selected for appropriate vocabulary level.
All verses are taken from ***The Living Bible***, Tyndale House Publishers, Wheaton, Illinois 60187. Used by permission.

Please, Help Us Hold Down Costs!

Photocopy machines are wonderful inventions, but did you know that it's ILLEGAL to reproduce copyrighted material?

Years of work and hundreds of thousands of dollars have gone into the development and production of A Reason For Handwriting®. Only your Christian integrity can help us avoid unnecessary price increases due to ILLEGAL photocopying.

Thank you for honoring copyright laws and not yielding to the temptation to "run off a few copies." It's not cost effective and it's ILLEGAL as well!

Attention Parents & Teachers:

Don't Settle for HALF a Curriculum!

A Reason For Handwriting® **Student Worktexts** integrate faith and learning by featuring lessons based on Scripture verses and built-in opportunities for sharing God's Word with others.

But, the **A Reason For Handwriting®** curriculum offers much, much more!

The **Comprehensive K-6th Teacher Guidebook** is full of essential instructions, helpful tips, and teacher-tested techniques to help you make the most of your handwriting practice.

Key instructional information in the **Teacher Guidebook** includes:

- **The Suggested Weekly Schedule**
- **Daily Lesson Plans**
- **Tips for Teaching Cursive Handwriting**
- **Techniques for Grading**

Plus the **Teacher Guidebook** includes a wealth of teacher-tested tips and enrichment ideas:

- **A Comprehesive Skills Index**
- **Extended Activities**
- **Ways to Share Border Sheets**
- **Letter Formation Charts**
- **Tips for Proper Positioning**
- **Letter Group Charts**
- **Vocabulary Lists**
- **Common Handwriting Problems**
- **Black Line Masters**

Just For Kids!

Welcome to A Reason For Handwriting®

This year you'll learn to write better, memorize Scripture, share God's Word, and have FUN!

Each week you'll practice letters and groups of letters from a different Scripture verse. Then you'll write the entire verse on practice paper. At the end of each week you'll pick a Scripture Border Sheet from the back of your Worktext, write the verse in your very best handwriting, and use your creative talents to color and decorate it. Now comes the really FUN part: Sharing God's Word!

You can share God's Word, in your very own handwriting, by giving people your finished Scripture Border Sheets! You can take them to nursing homes, share them with friends, make placemats for your kitchen table, mail them to someone who isn't feeling well. . . you get the idea. And we're sure you'll come up with even more ideas throughout the year!

And sharing God's Word with others gives you the very best reason for improving your handwriting!

Meet New Friends

Throughout this book, you'll see illustrations of kids like you who are caring, sharing, working, and learning. Be sure to watch for these new faces!

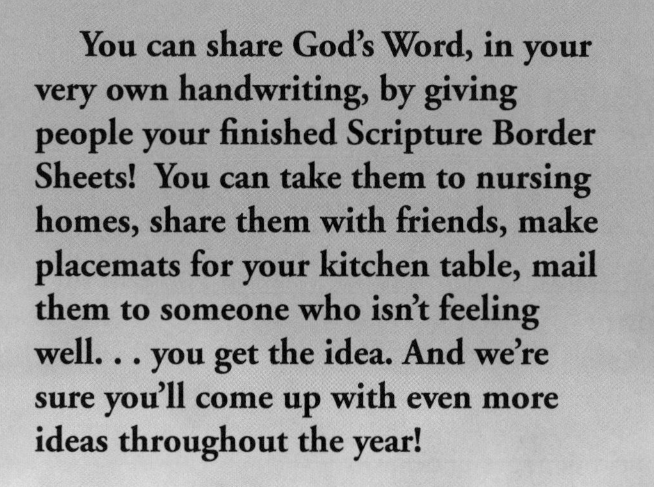

How to Become A Five Star Student!

Do you want your writing to look its very best? Here are the five basic areas you should consider when evaluating your handwriting form:

Alignment
Each letter or word should sit *on* the line, not above or below it.

Slant
Letters slant must be consistent with the edge of the paper, or with other downstroke letters.

Size
Capital letters are all one full space tall. The lowercase letters b, d, f, h, k, l, and t are also one space tall. All other lowercase letters are half a space tall. Also, letters that go below the line (g, j, p, q, and y) should extend to the bottom line.

Shape
Letters should be uniform and easy to read. When letters are written with correct strokes, they have a more consistent look.

Spacing
Letters should not run into each other, or be too far apart. Allow a letter space (o) between words and sentences.

Follow these guidelines, focusing on consistency and quality, and you'll be a **Five Star** student!

The following practice sentence contains all the letters of the alphabet:

God created zebras and foxes to walk, jump, and hide very quickly.

Practice
Lessons
C

After the summer break, students often benefit from a focused review. The following **Practice Lessons** provide a quick, efficient method for reviewing manuscript letter formation.

These lessons are designed for one page each day, for a total of 6 weeks.

Another option is to begin immediately with Lesson 1 (page 41), and use these review pages as concurrent extra practice.

Practice

Lesson 5

Name

a

d

dad

do

Name

g g

q q

dog

go

Name

b

e

be

bed

Name

p p

i i

pig

did

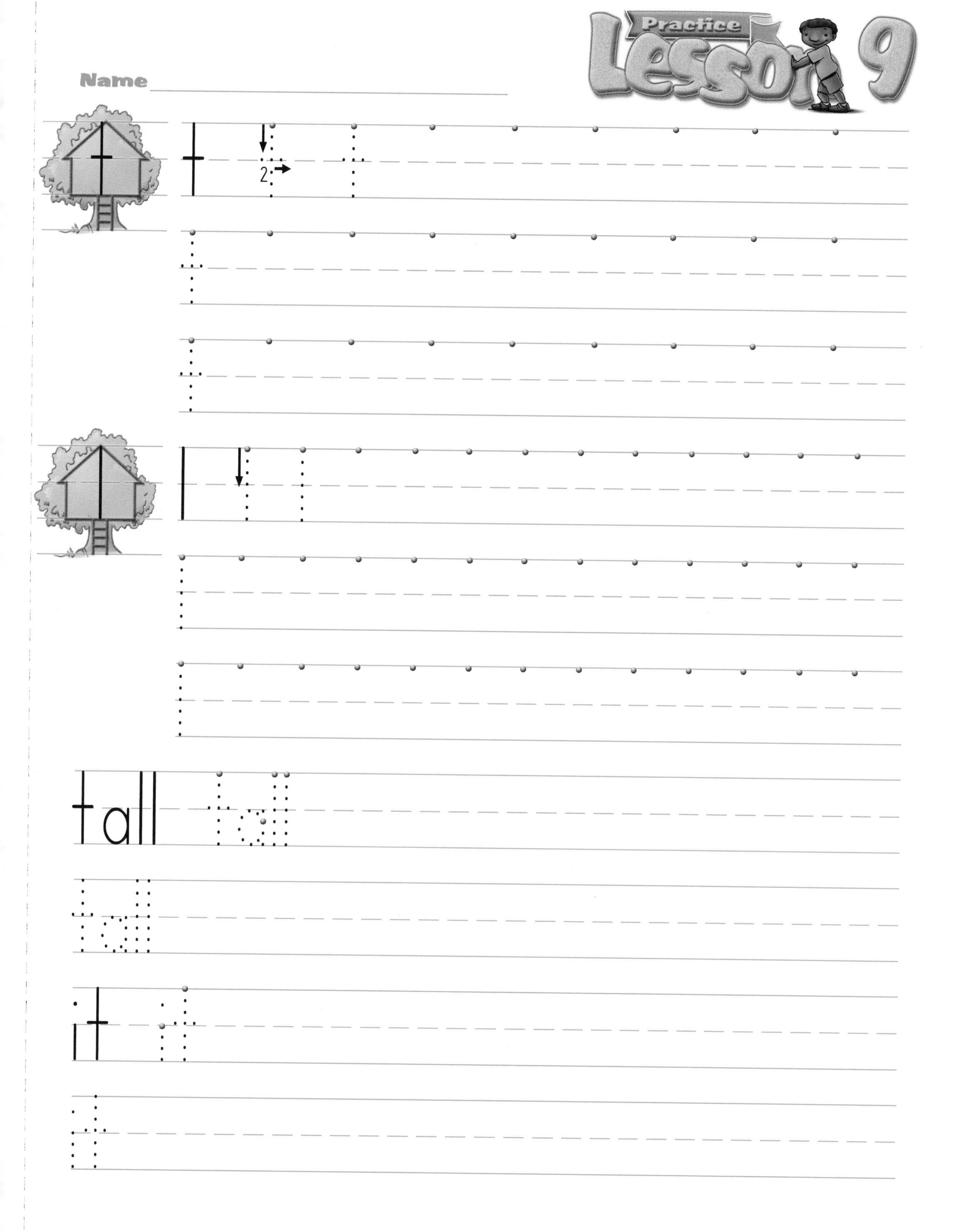
Practice
Lesson 9
Name
t
2
l
tall
it

Name ______________________

h h

r r

hat

rat

Name

n

m

not

man

Name ____________________

f f

k k

fill

kind

Name ____________________

j j j j

y y y y

jet jet

jet

may may

may

Name ______________________

v

w

vine

want

Name ______________________

u u u u

u

u

s s s s

s

s

yes yes

yes

us us

us

Name

X X

x

x

Z Z

z

z

ax

ax

ax

zoo

zoo

zoo

Name ______________________________

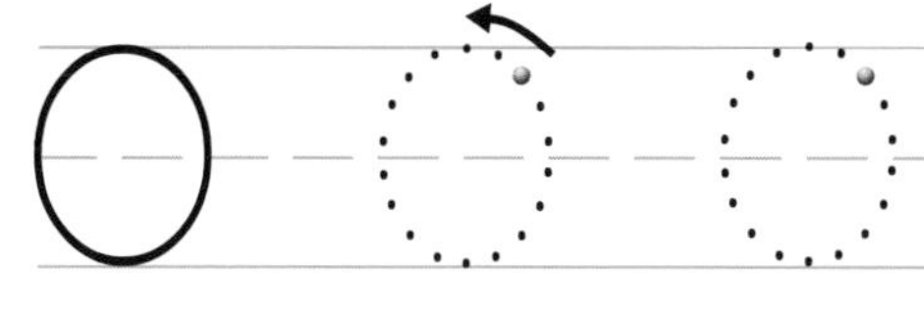

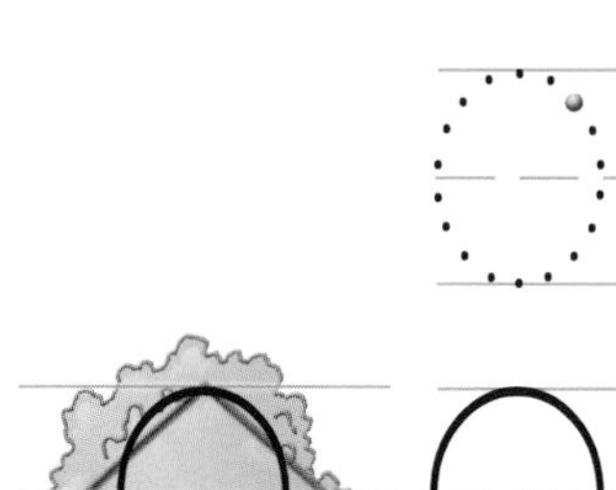
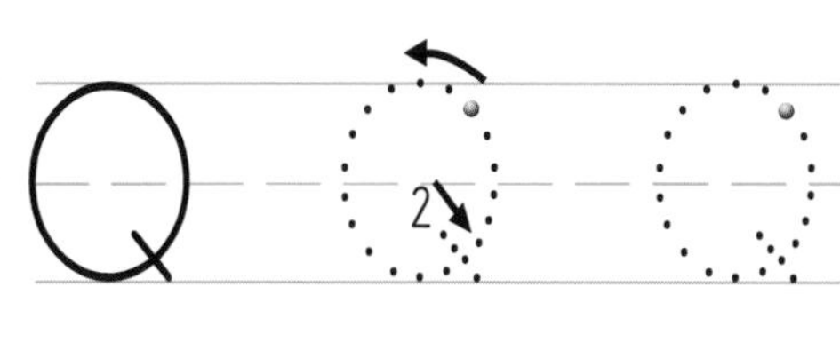

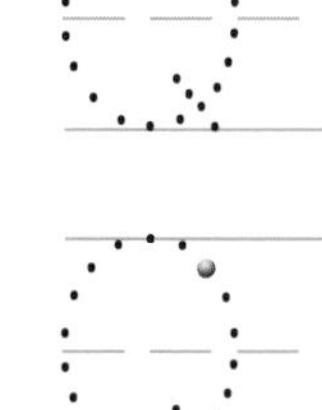

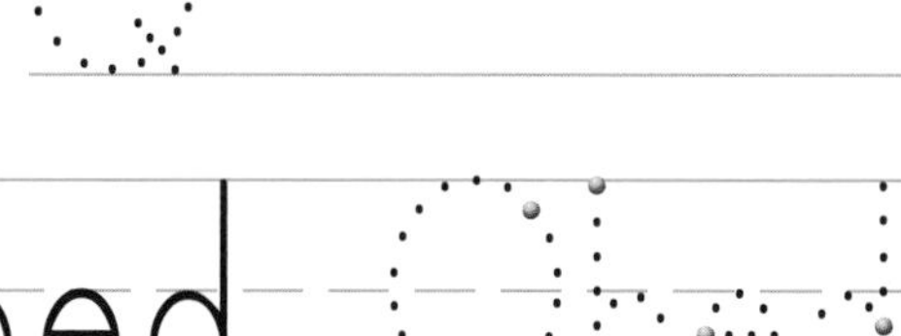

Obed

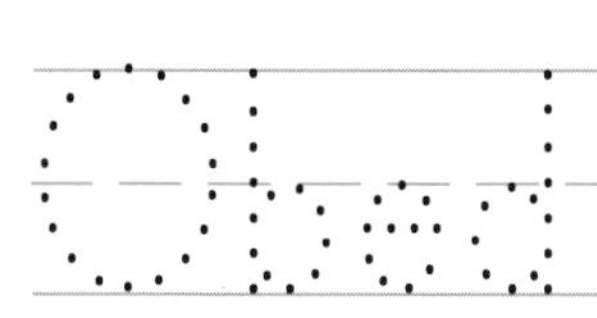

Queen

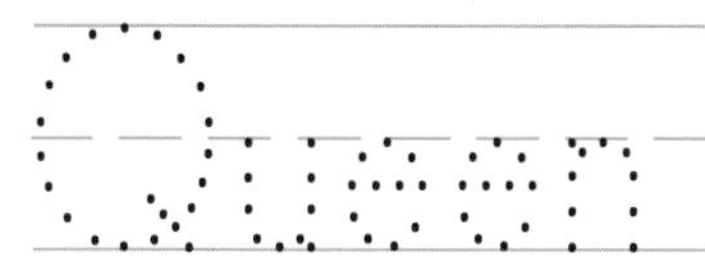

Name

C C C C

G G G G

Christ Christ

Christ

God God

God

Name ______________________

P P

B B

Paul

Bible

Name ______________________

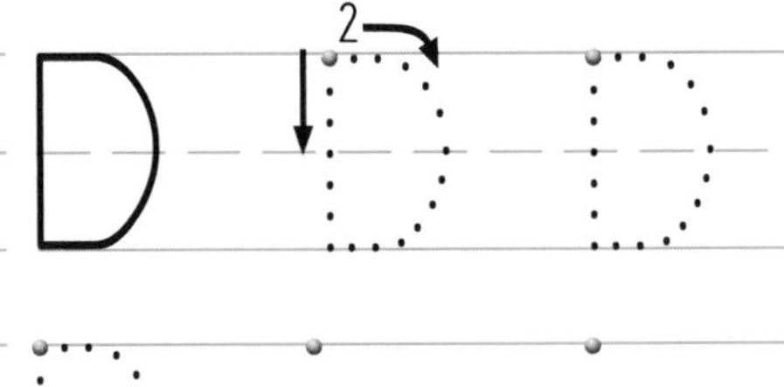

D

D

R 2 R R

R

R

David David

David

Ruth Ruth

Ruth

Name

F 1 2 3

E 1 2 3

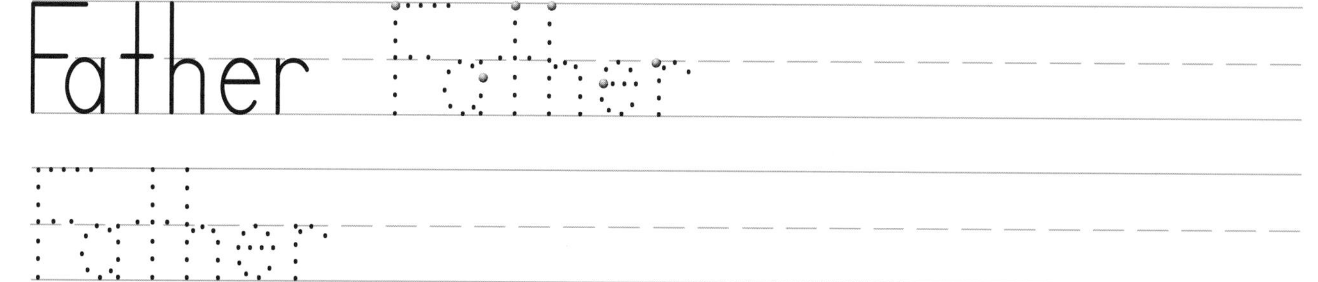

Father Father

Father

Eve Eve

Eve

Name

Practice Lesson 23

Name ______________________________

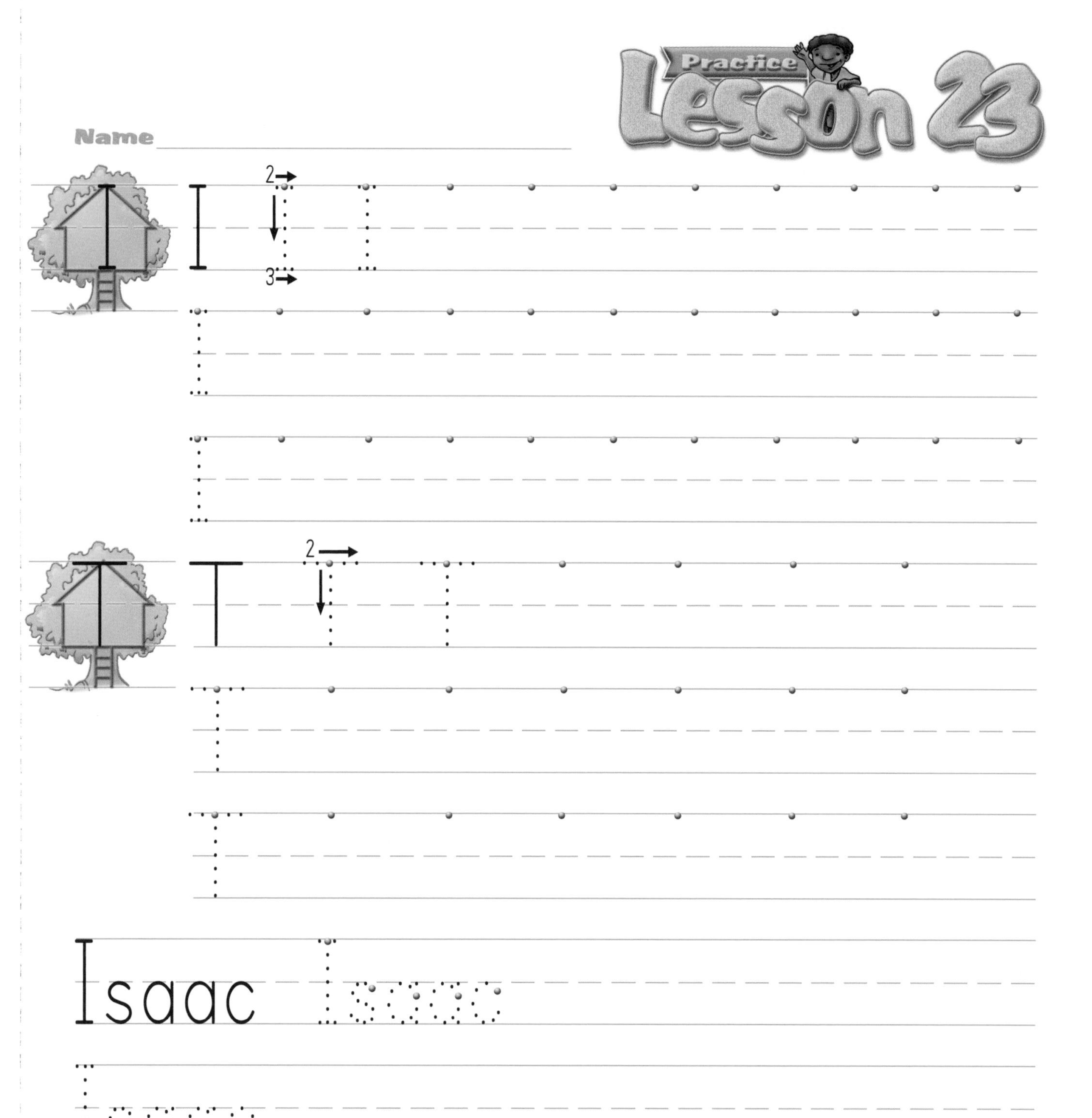

Isaac Isaac

Isaac

Terah Terah

Terah

K K K

K

K

L L L

L

L

King King

King

Luke Luke

Luke

Name

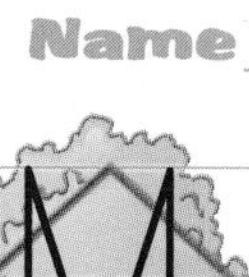

M M M M

M

M

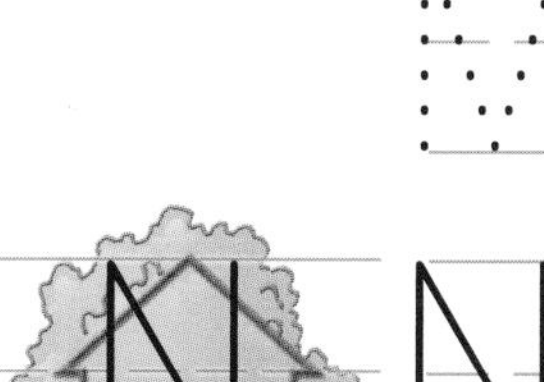

N N N N

N

N

Mary Mary

Mary

Naomi Naomi

Naomi

Practice Lesson 26

Name ______________________

A

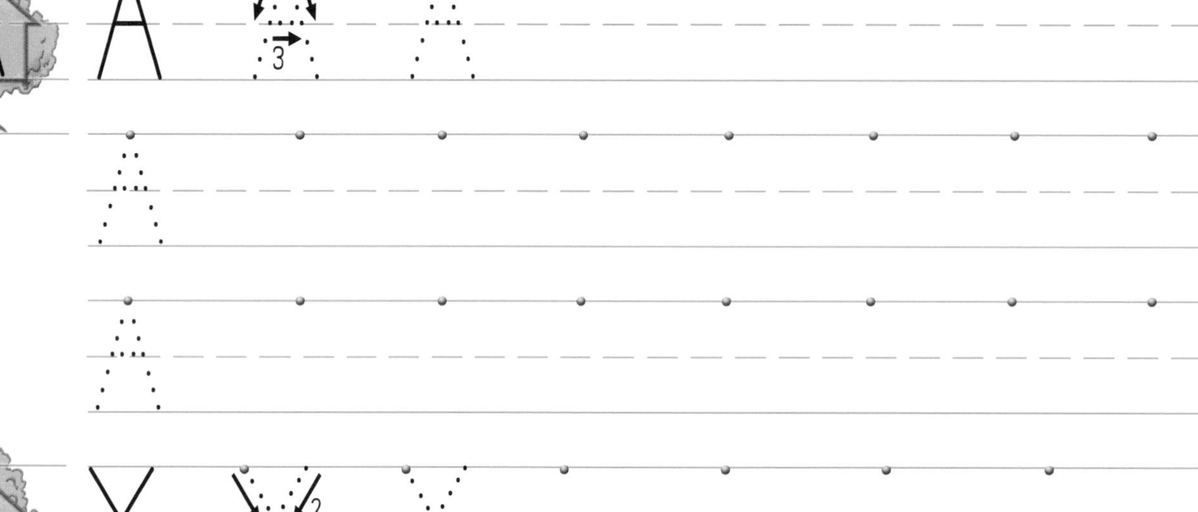

X

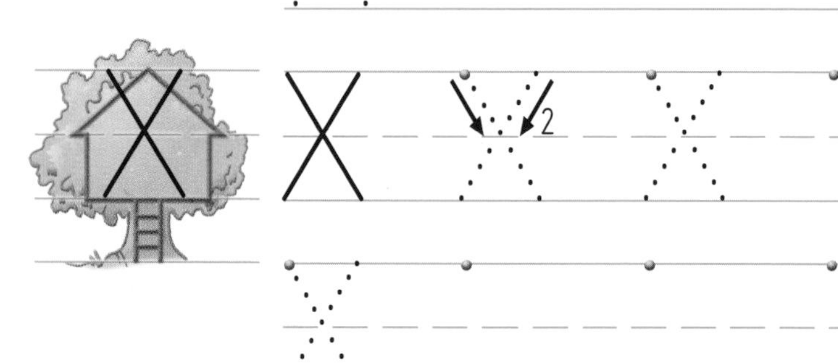

Adam

Xerxes

Name

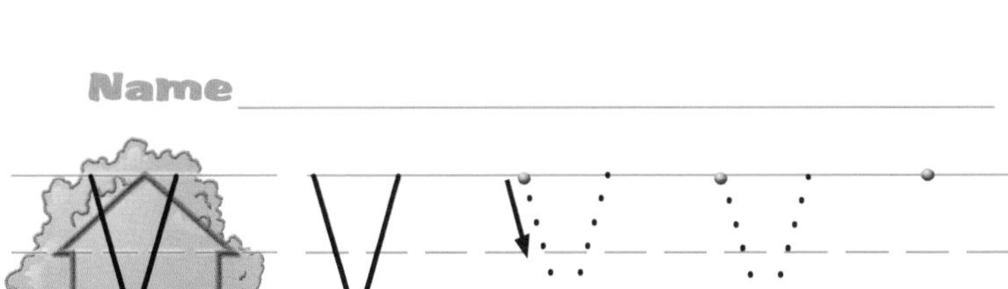

V V V

W W W

Vashti Vashti

Vashti

Word Word

Word

Practice
Lesson 28
Name
J J
S S
Jesus
Samuel

Name

Y Y Y

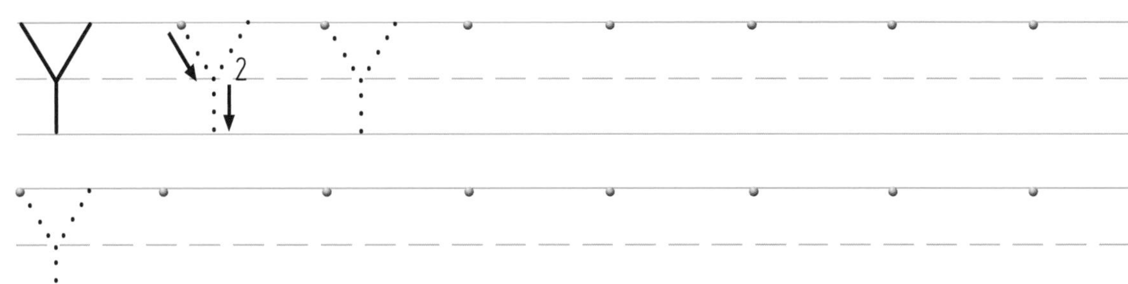

Y

Y

Z Z Z

Z

Z

Yahweh Yahweh

Yahweh

Zion Zion

Zion

Name ______________________

Aa Bb Cc Dd Ee Ff
Gg Hh Ii Jj Kk Ll Mm
Nn Oo Pp Qq Rr Ss
Tt Uu Vv Ww Xx Yy
Zz 0 1 2 3 4 5 6 7 8 9

Daily
Lessons
C

Before beginning instruction, please review the **Weekly Lesson Format** (Teacher Guidebook, page 56). Here you will find detailed directions for implementing the 5-day format, as well as suggestions for using the **Scripture Border Sheets**.

Careful review of this material at the start of the school year will greatly enhance the effectiveness of this curriculum.

Name ______________________________

The capital A looks like a teepee with a line in the middle. The lowercase a is easy to write since it begins just like the lowercase o.

Day One Practice the following letters and words from this week's Scripture.

Aa Aa

Aa

All All

All

Day Two Continue practicing letters and words from this week's Scripture.

that that

that

done done

done

Day Three

Practice the final letters and words from this week's Scripture.

day day
day

long long
long

have have
have

Day Four

Practice this week's entire Scripture verse by tracing over each of the letters below.

All day long I'll praise and honor You, oh God, for all that You have done for me.

Psalm 71:8

Name ________________

The capital and lowercase **c**'s look alike, but are different sizes. Try to make your **c**'s very round. Make certain the capital C touches the top and bottom lines.

Day One Practice the following letters and words from this week's Scripture.

Cc

count

Day Two Continue practicing letters and words from this week's Scripture.

counting

should

Day Three

Practice the final letters and words from this week's Scripture.

us us

us

plans plans

plans

make make

make

Day Four

Practice this week's entire Scripture verse by tracing over each of the letters below.

We should make plans—
counting on God to direct us.
Proverbs 16:9

Name

It's easier to remember how to write the lowercase d if you begin it like the c: around, up, then back down.

Day One

Practice the following letters and words from this week's Scripture.

Dd Dd

Dd

does does

does

Day Two

Continue practicing letters and words from this week's Scripture.

delights delights

delights

those those

those

Day Three

Practice the final letters and words from this week's Scripture.

keep keep

keep

promises promises

promises

who who

who

Day Four

Practice this week's entire Scripture verse by tracing over each of the letters below.

God delights in those

who keep their promises.

Proverbs 12:22

FIDO

Name

Tip of the Week

The bottom part of the lowercase g is like a monkey's tail. It goes down the ladder all the way to the ground! Be sure to write the g without picking up your pencil.

Day One

Practice the following letters and words from this week's Scripture.

Gg Gg

Gg

God God

God

Day Two

Continue practicing letters and words from this week's Scripture.

praise praise

praise

new new

new

Day Three

Practice the final letters and words from this week's Scripture.

songs songs

songs

compose compose

compose

of of

of

Day Four

Practice this week's entire Scripture verse by tracing over each of the letters below.

Compose new songs of praise to God.

Psalm 33:3

Name

The capital letter E is written with three strokes. Start by making a capital L, then go across the top, then across the middle.

Day One Practice the following letters and words from this week's Scripture.

Ee Ee

Ee

earth earth

earth

Day Two Continue practicing letters and words from this week's Scripture.

belongs belongs

belongs

His His

His

Day Three

Practice the final letters and words from this week's Scripture.

the the

the

Everything Everything

Everything

world world

world

Day Four

Practice this week's entire Scripture verse by tracing over each of the letters below.

The earth belongs to God! Everything in all the world is His!

Psalm 24:1

Name ______________________________

The lowercase q looks like the g, but the q's tail curves to the right. The capital Q looks a lot like an O, but the added line makes it unique. Write your q's carefully this week!

Day One

Practice the following letters and words from this week's Scripture.

Qq Qq

Qq

quarrel quarrel

quarrel

Day Two

Continue practicing letters and words from this week's Scripture.

hard hard

hard

once once

once

Day Three

Practice the final letters and words from this week's Scripture.

begin begin

begin

stop stop

stop

so so

so

Day Four

Practice this week's entire Scripture verse by tracing over each of the letters below.

It is hard to stop a quarrel once it starts, so don't let it begin.

Proverbs 17:14

Name ________________________

Think of the lowercase **b** as a baseball bat standing on end with a ball connected to it. To write the **b**, go down, up, and around. Spend time this week "Sky Writing" the **b**.

Day One Practice the following letters and words from this week's Scripture.

Bb

Be

Day Two Continue practicing letters and words from this week's Scripture.

become

wise

Day Three

Practice the final letters and words from this week's Scripture.

men men

men

with with

with

evil evil

evil

Day Four

Practice this week's entire Scripture verse by tracing over each of the letters below.

Be with wise men and

become wise. Be with evil

men and become evil.

Proverbs 13:20

Name ______________________________

Remember, your name is the most important word you write! To make it as special as you are, make certain you take time to write it clearly and carefully.

Day One Practice the following letters and words from this week's Scripture.

Pp

Help

Day Two Continue practicing letters and words from this week's Scripture.

you

do

Day Three

Practice the final letters and words from this week's Scripture.

paths paths

paths

lead lead

lead

are are

are

Day Four

Practice this week's entire Scripture verse by tracing over each of the letters below.

Help me to do your will, for You are my God. Lead me in good paths.

Psalm 143:10

Name

Tip of the Week

Vowels are important letters. Every word has a vowel: **a, e, i, o, u** (and sometimes **y**). As you write your vowels this week, pay close attention to their shape and size.

Day One

Practice the following letters and words from this week's Scripture.

Ee Ee

Ee

puts puts

puts

Day Two

Continue practicing letters and words from this week's Scripture.

blesses blesses

blesses

trust trust

trust

Day Three

Practice the final letters and words from this week's Scripture.

obey obey

obey

happy happy

happy

man man

man

Day Four

Practice this week's entire Scripture verse by tracing over each of the letters below.

God blesses those who obey Him; happy the man who puts his trust in the Lord. Proverbs 16:20

Name ______________________

Sometimes the letter **I** is used as a word by itself. When **I** is a word, it is always capitalized. What other capitalized word do you write every day? (Hint: you sign your papers with it.)

Day One

Practice the following letters and words from this week's Scripture.

Ii Ii

I

will will

will

Day Two

Continue practicing letters and words from this week's Scripture.

richly richly

richly

I I

I

Day Three

Practice the final letters and words from this week's Scripture.

sing sing

sing

has has

has

because because

because

Day Four

Practice this week's entire Scripture verse by tracing over each of the letters below.

I will sing to the Lord
because He has blessed me
so richly. Psalm 13:6

Name ______________________________

The capital and lowercase t's look very different, but they are similar, too! Both t's are tall letters, and both of them have a second stroke.

Day One

Practice the following letters and words from this week's Scripture.

Tt Tt

Tt

To To

To

Day Two

Continue practicing letters and words from this week's Scripture.

poor poor

poor

the the

the

Day Three

Practice the final letters and words from this week's Scripture.

honor honor

honor

help help

help

is is

is

Day Four

Practice this week's entire Scripture verse by tracing over each of the letters below.

To help the poor is to honor God.

Proverbs 14:31

Name ____________________

Tip of the Week

The capital and lowercase l's are both tall letters. They look a lot alike, but the capital L needs a leg to stand on! Make your l's as straight as you can.

Day One Practice the following letters and words from this week's Scripture.

Ll Ll

Ll

Lord's Lord's

Lord's

Day Two Continue practicing letters and words from this week's Scripture.

blessing blessing

blessing

our our

our

Day Three

Practice the final letters and words from this week's Scripture.

wealth wealth

wealth

greatest greatest

greatest

Proverbs Proverbs

Proverbs

Day Four

Practice this week's entire Scripture verse by tracing over each of the letters below.

The Lord's blessing is our greatest wealth.

Proverbs 10:22

Name ______________________

The capital letter H is a three-stroke letter. Go down, down, and across. How is this similar to the capital A? How is it different?

Day One Practice the following letters and words from this week's Scripture.

Hh

wish

Day Two Continue practicing letters and words from this week's Scripture.

me

love

Day Three

Practice the final letters and words from this week's Scripture.

Help Help

Help

every every

every

Your Your

Your

Day Four

Practice this week's entire Scripture verse by tracing over each of the letters below.

Help me to love Your every wish.

Psalm 119:80

Name ________________________________

Tip of the Week

As you write the lowercase **r**,
don't pick up your pencil. Go down,
up, and curve around — but not too far!

Day One

Practice the following letters and words from this week's Scripture.

Rr Rr

Rr

fort fort

fort

Day Two

Continue practicing letters and words from this week's Scripture.

enter enter

enter

safe safe

safe

Day Three

Practice the final letters and words from this week's Scripture.

Lord Lord

Lord

where where

where

can can

can

Day Four

Practice this week's entire Scripture verse by tracing over each of the letters below.

The Lord is my fort where I can enter and be safe. Psalm 18:2

Name ______________________________

Compare the lowercase **n** with the **h**, **r**, and **m**.
Even though they are a lot alike, each one is a little different.
God made each of us a little different, too — that's what makes us special!

Day One

Practice the following letters and words from this week's Scripture.

Nn Nn

Nn

Never Never

Never

Day Two

Continue practicing letters and words from this week's Scripture.

truthful truthful

truthful

to to

to

Day Three

Practice the final letters and words from this week's Scripture.

kind kind

kind

forget forget

forget

and and

and

Day Four

Practice this week's entire Scripture verse by tracing over each of the letters below.

Never forget to be truthful and kind.

Proverbs 3:3

Name ________________________________

Remember, you only pick your pencil up once as you write the capital **M**. The same is true for the capital **N**. Practice these letters, describing the strokes as you write them.

Day One Practice the following letters and words from this week's Scripture.

Mm Mm

Mm

me me

me

Day Two Continue practicing letters and words from this week's Scripture.

along along

along

tell tell

tell

Day Three

Practice the final letters and words from this week's Scripture.

Make Make

Make

right right

right

walk walk

walk

Day Four

Practice this week's entire Scripture verse by tracing over each of the letters below.

Just tell me what to do and I will do it, Lord. Make me walk along the right paths. Psalm 119:33,35

Name ____________________

Our focus letters this week are the capital and lowercase **a** and **o**. See how many words you can find this week that contain the circle letters **a** or **o**.

Day One Practice the following letters and words from this week's Scripture.

Aa Aa

Aa

Oo Oo

Oo

Day Two Continue practicing letters and words from this week's Scripture.

loyal loyal

loyal

brother brother

brother

Day Three

Practice the final letters and words from this week's Scripture.

always always

always

time time

time

born born

born

Day Four

Practice this week's entire Scripture verse by tracing over each of the letters below.

A true friend is always loyal and a brother is born to help in time of need.

Proverbs 17:17

Name

The capital letter F is a "three-stroke" letter.
The capital letter E is also a three-stroke letter.
Which stroke makes the E different from the capital F?

Day One Practice the following letters and words from this week's Scripture.

Ff

Fill

Day Two Continue practicing letters and words from this week's Scripture.

from

with

Day Three Practice the final letters and words from this week's Scripture.

after after

after

happiness happiness

happiness

face face

face

Day Four Practice this week's entire Scripture verse by tracing over each of the letters below.

Fill all who love You with

Your happiness.

Psalm 5:11

Name ______________________________

Tip of the Week

Make certain your paper is slanted the same direction as your writing arm. This will make it much easier to keep your letters straight as you write.

Day One Practice the following letters and words from this week's Scripture.

Uu Uu

Uu

upon upon

upon

Day Two Continue practicing letters and words from this week's Scripture.

delight delight

delight

law law

law

Day Three

Practice the final letters and words from this week's Scripture.

Day Four

Practice this week's entire Scripture verse by tracing over each of the letters below.

Name ______________________________

Here's a trick to help you remember how to form the capital and lowercase j's. Think about the shape of the staff that David (the shepherd boy) used to reach down and rescue a fallen lamb.

Day One

Practice the following letters and words from this week's Scripture.

Jj

Joy

Day Two

Continue practicing letters and words from this week's Scripture.

rises

burst

Day Three

Practice the final letters and words from this week's Scripture.

songs songs

songs

just just

just

until until

until

Day Four

Practice this week's entire Scripture verse by tracing over each of the letters below.

Joy rises in my heart
until I burst out in songs of
praise to God.

Psalm 28:7

Name ______________________

The capital and lowercase Y are two-stroke letters. Practice these letters describing the strokes as you write.

Day One Practice the following letters and words from this week's Scripture.

Yy Yy

Yy

You You

You

Day Two Continue practicing letters and words from this week's Scripture.

my my

my

laws laws

laws

Day Three

Practice the final letters and words from this week's Scripture.

body body

body

Your Your

Your

heed heed

heed

Day Four

Practice this week's entire Scripture verse by tracing over each of the letters below.

You made my body, Lord;

now give me sense to heed

Your laws.

Psalm 119:73

Name ______________________________

It's a lot easier to make the sharp point
on the lowercase **v** if your pencil is sharp, too.
Slant down, slant up — and don't pick up your pencil!

Day One Practice the following letters and words from this week's Scripture.

Vv Vv

Vv

very very

very

Day Two Continue practicing letters and words from this week's Scripture.

Proverbs Proverbs

Proverbs

He He

He

Day Three

Practice the final letters and words from this week's Scripture.

direct direct

direct

put put

put

first first

first

Day Four

Practice this week's entire Scripture verse by tracing over each of the letters below.

In everything you do, put God first, and He will direct you.

Proverbs 3:6

Name ___________________________

Tip of the Week

Both the capital and lowercase **W**'s look like two **V**'s that are stuck together. For extra practice, "Sky Write" the **W**'s while saying the strokes aloud: down, up, down, up.

Day One

Practice the following letters and words from this week's Scripture.

Ww Ww

Ww

What What

What

Day Two

Continue practicing letters and words from this week's Scripture.

thing thing

thing

know know

know

Day Three

Practice the final letters and words from this week's Scripture.

nation nation

nation

it it

it

wonderful wonderful

wonderful

Day Four

Practice this week's entire Scripture verse by tracing over each of the letters below.

What a wonderful thing
it is for a nation to know
and keep God's laws!
Proverbs 29:18

Name ______________________

Tip of the Week

Here's another trick to help you remember a letter shape. There's a **v** hidden in both the capital and lowercase **k**'s. Can you see it? (Hint: turn your head sideways.)

Day One

Practice the following letters and words from this week's Scripture.

Kk Kk

Kk

Kind Kind

Kind

Day Two

Continue practicing letters and words from this week's Scripture.

enjoyable enjoyable

enjoyable

words words

words

Day Three

Practice the final letters and words from this week's Scripture.

like like

like

honey honey

honey

healthful healthful

healthful

Day Four

Practice this week's entire Scripture verse by tracing over each of the letters below.

Kind words are like

honey—enjoyable and

healthful.

Proverbs 16:24

Name

Tip of the Week

When you think of the letter **s**, think of a snake and the sound it makes — hiss! Both the capital and lowercase **s** look a little like a snake, and they make the "hiss" sound, too.

Day One Practice the following letters and words from this week's Scripture.

Ss Ss

Ss

Sing Sing

Sing

Day Two Continue practicing letters and words from this week's Scripture.

someone someone

someone

Each Each

Each

Day Three

Practice the final letters and words from this week's Scripture.

song song

song

saves saves

saves

Psalms Psalms

Psalms

Day Four

Practice this week's entire Scripture verse by tracing over each of the letters below.

Sing a new song to the Lord! Each day tell someone that He saves.

Psalm 96:1,2

Name ______________________________

Tip of the Week

You can make a giant letter X by crossing your arms in front of you. When you write the X, be sure you use two slanting downstrokes.

Day One

Practice the following letters and words from this week's Scripture.

Xx Xx

Xx

exciting exciting

exciting

Day Two

Continue practicing letters and words from this week's Scripture.

man's man's

man's

exit exit

exit

Day Three

Practice the final letters and words from this week's Scripture.

godly godly

godly

except except

except

life life

life

Day Four

Practice this week's entire Scripture verse by tracing over each of the letters below.

The godly man's life is exciting.

Proverbs 14:14

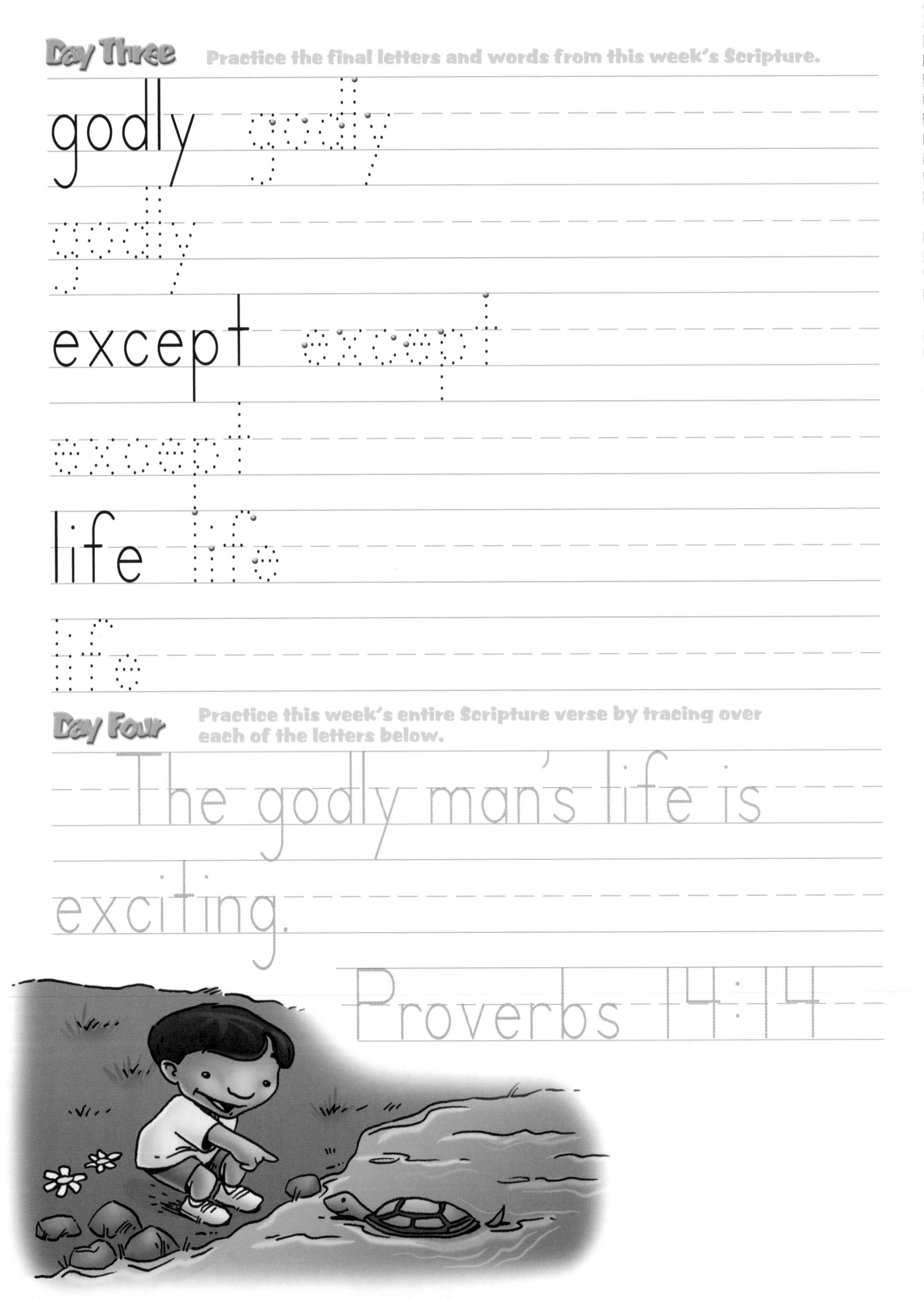

Name ______________________

Compare your writing now with your writing at the beginning of this Worktext. Doesn't it look much better? Remember, writing clearly and correctly is always worth the extra effort.

Day One Practice the following letters and words from this week's Scripture.

Zz Zz

Zz

Lazy Lazy

Lazy

Day Two Continue practicing letters and words from this week's Scripture.

get get

get

soon soon

soon

Day Three

Practice the final letters and words from this week's Scripture.

workers workers

workers

zip zip

zip

rich rich

rich

Day Four

Practice this week's entire Scripture verse by tracing over each of the letters below.

Lazy men are soon poor;
hard workers get rich.
Proverbs 10:4

SCRIPTURE
Border Sheets
FOR WEEKLY
SHARING
C

To The Teacher

The following pages are for use on Day 5 of the Weekly Lesson Format (Teacher Guidebook, page 56).

These Scripture Border Sheets not only provide a significant outreach component, but a strong motivational tool as well.

This section contains 31 Scripture Border Sheets — one per lesson, plus an extra, plus two blanks (pages 157 and 159) that allow for student-designed artwork.

For creative ways to use the Scripture Border Sheets see "Ways to Share" (Teacher Guidebook, page 58).

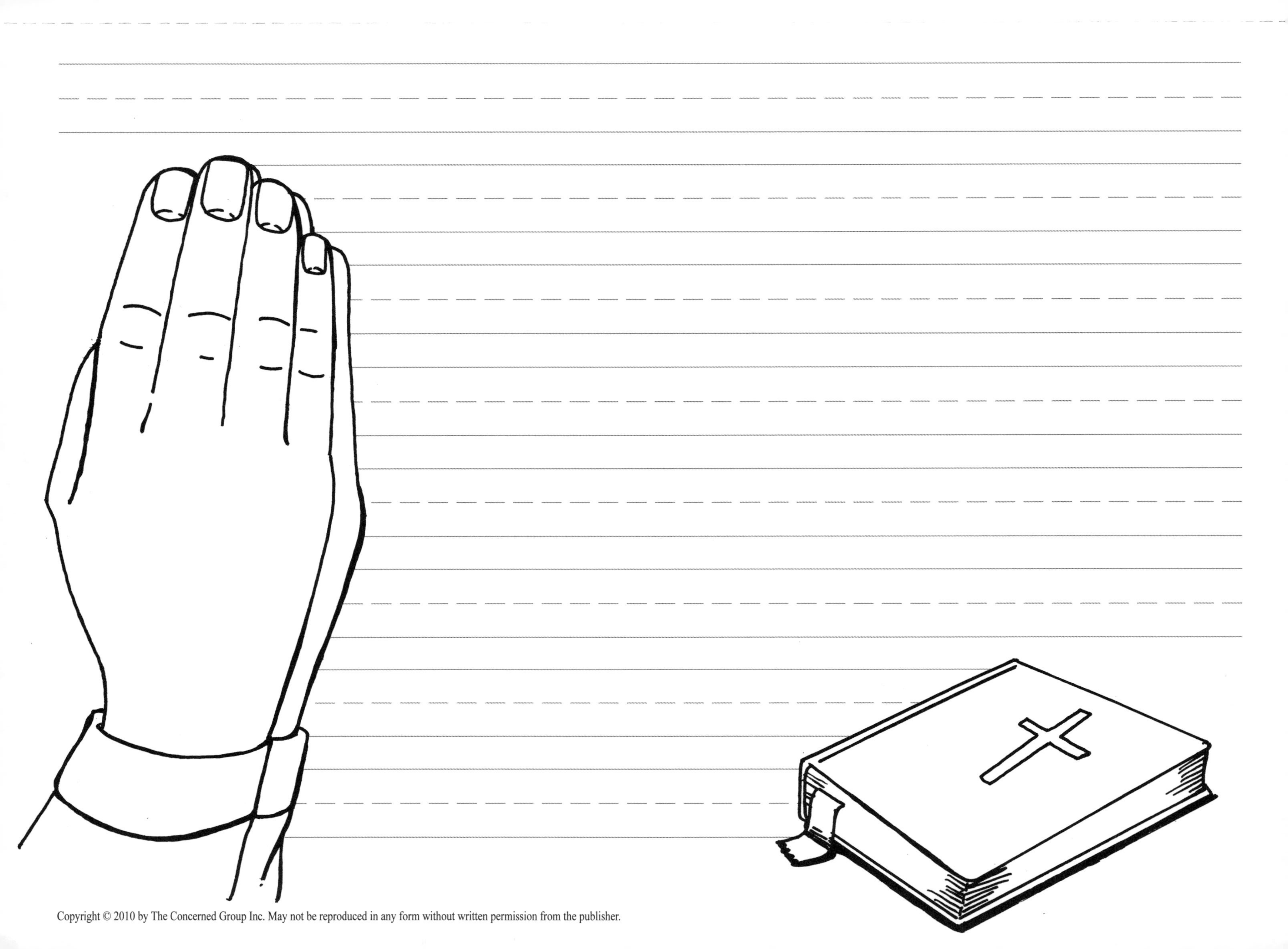

2+2=4
ABC

He is risen!

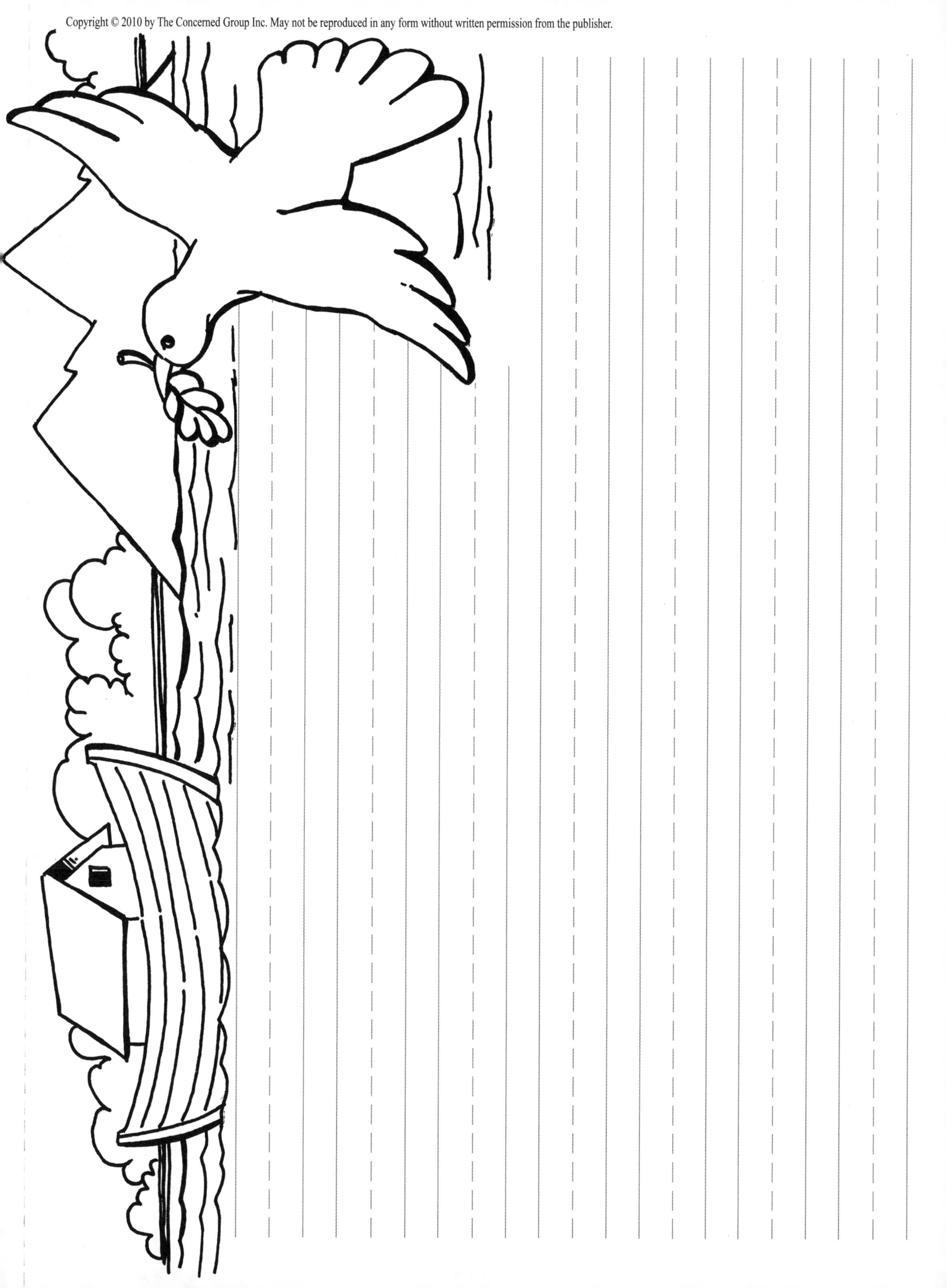

God Bless You

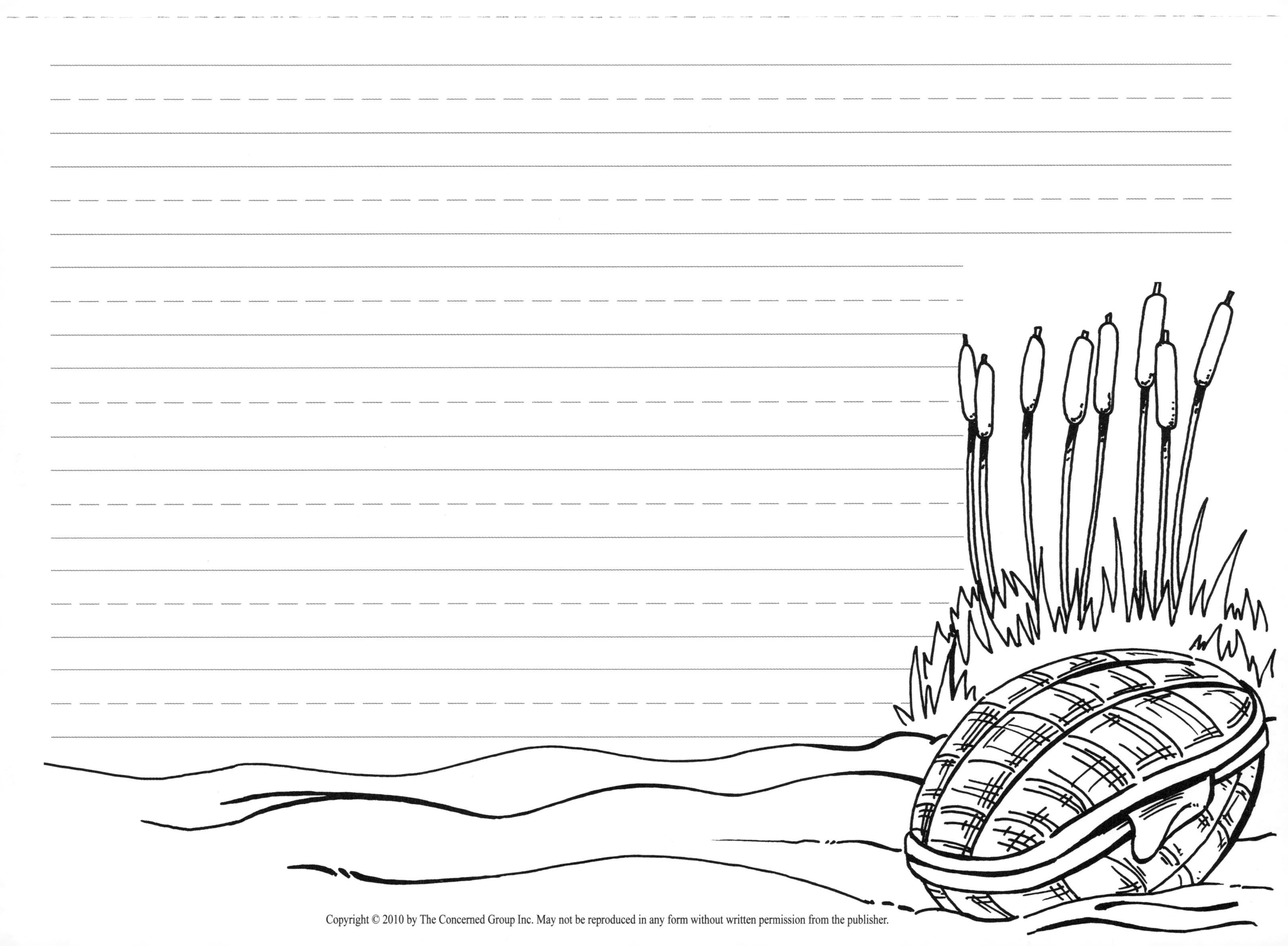

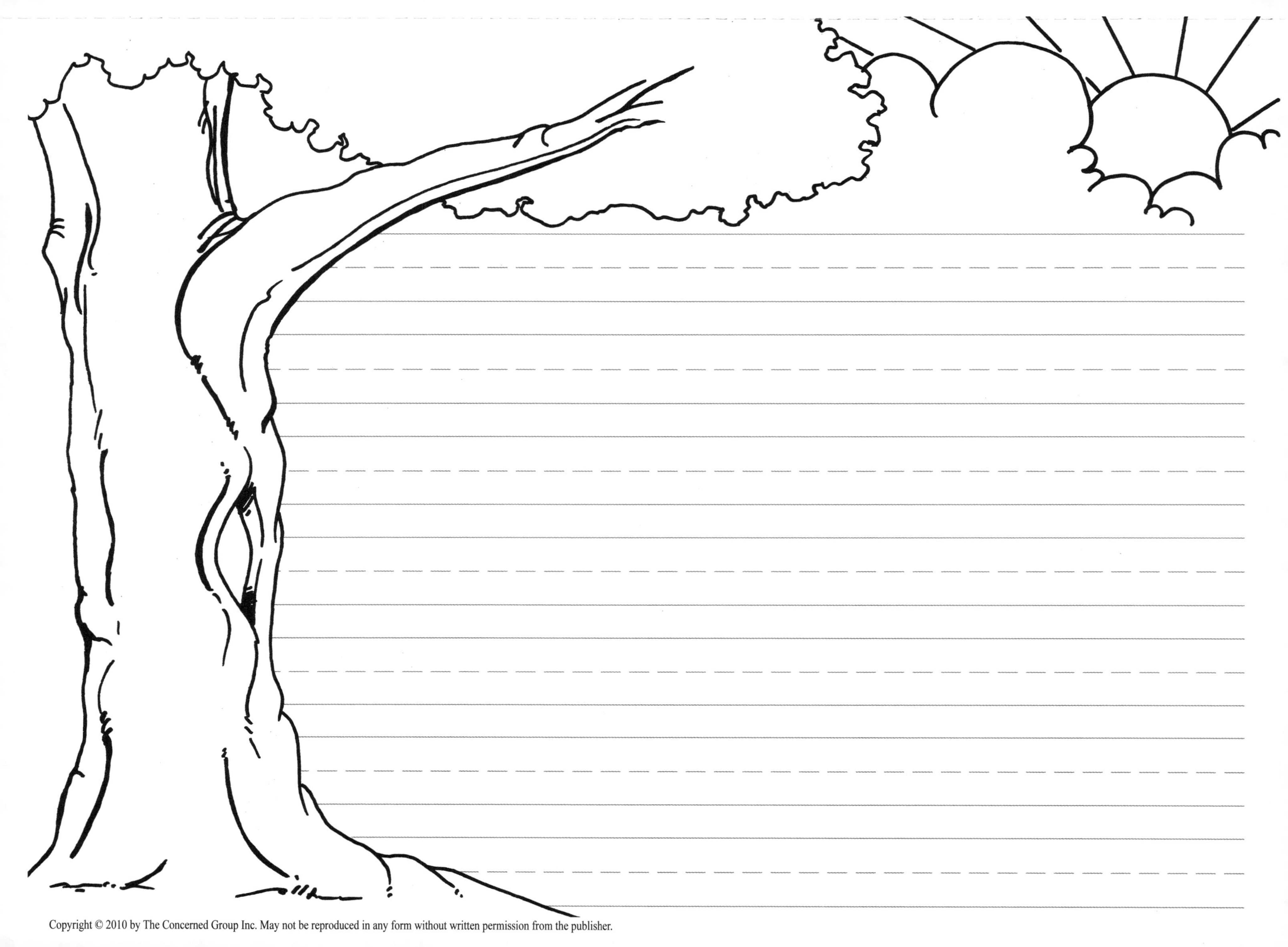

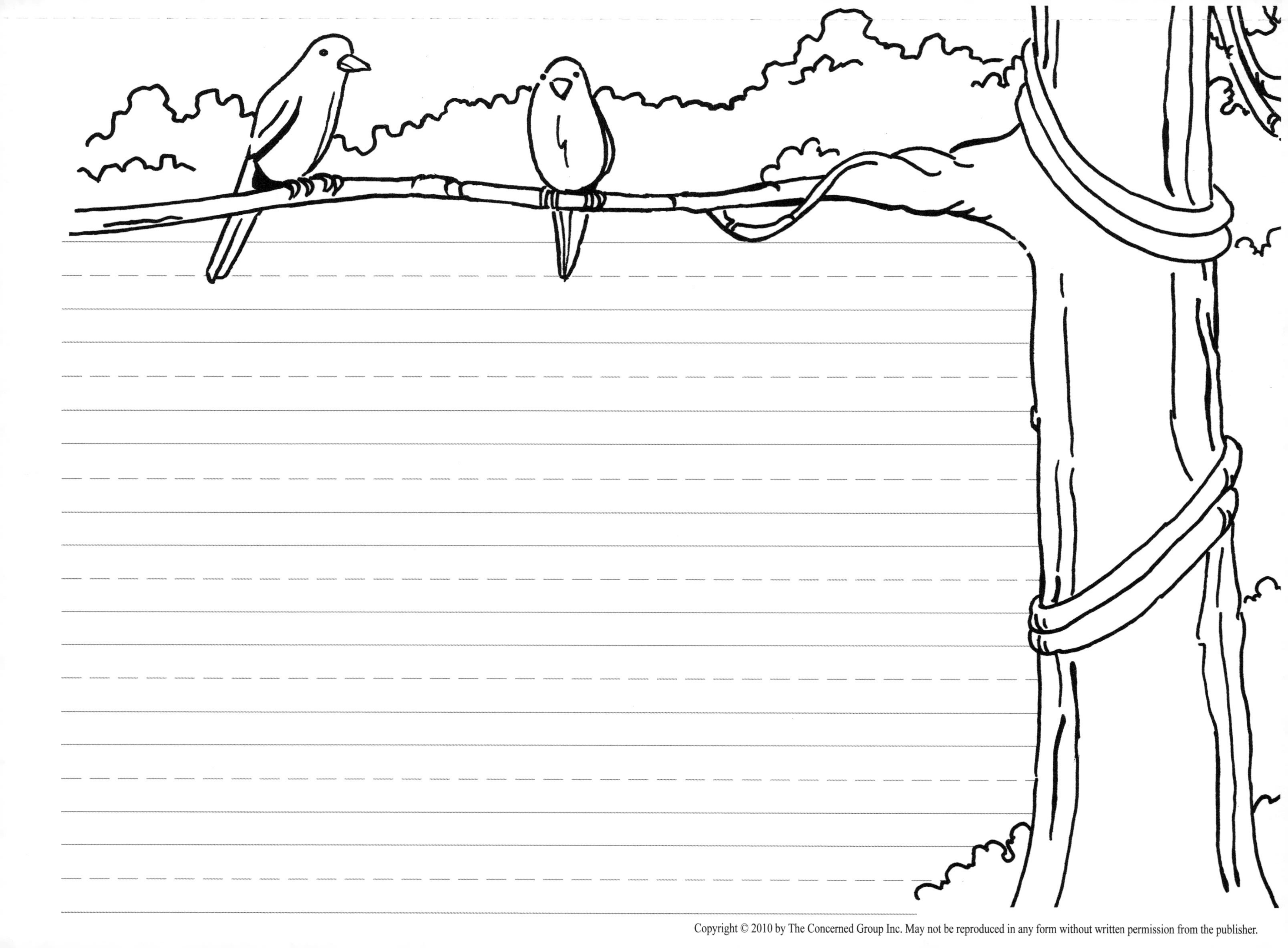

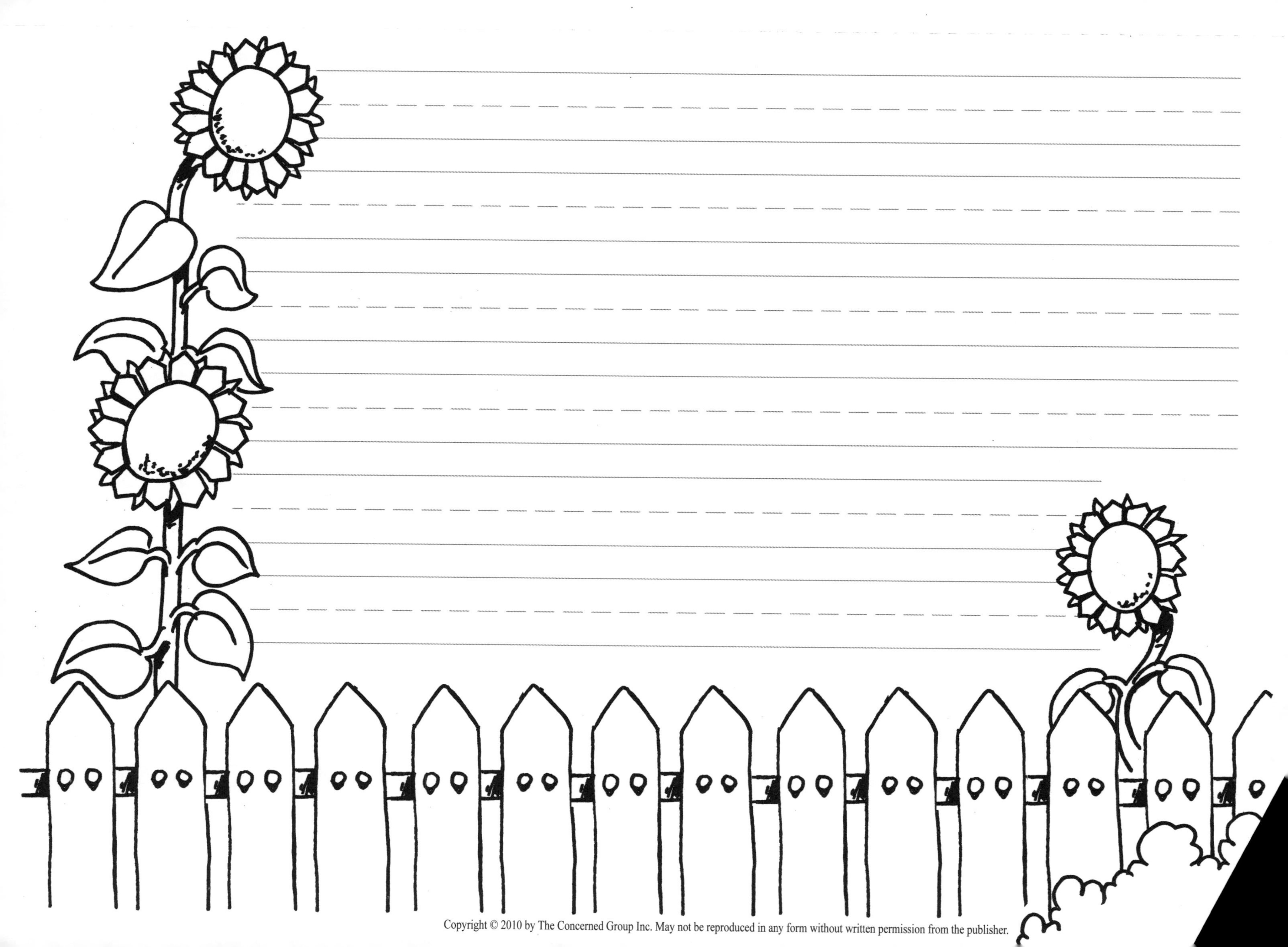

HAPPY
BIRTHD

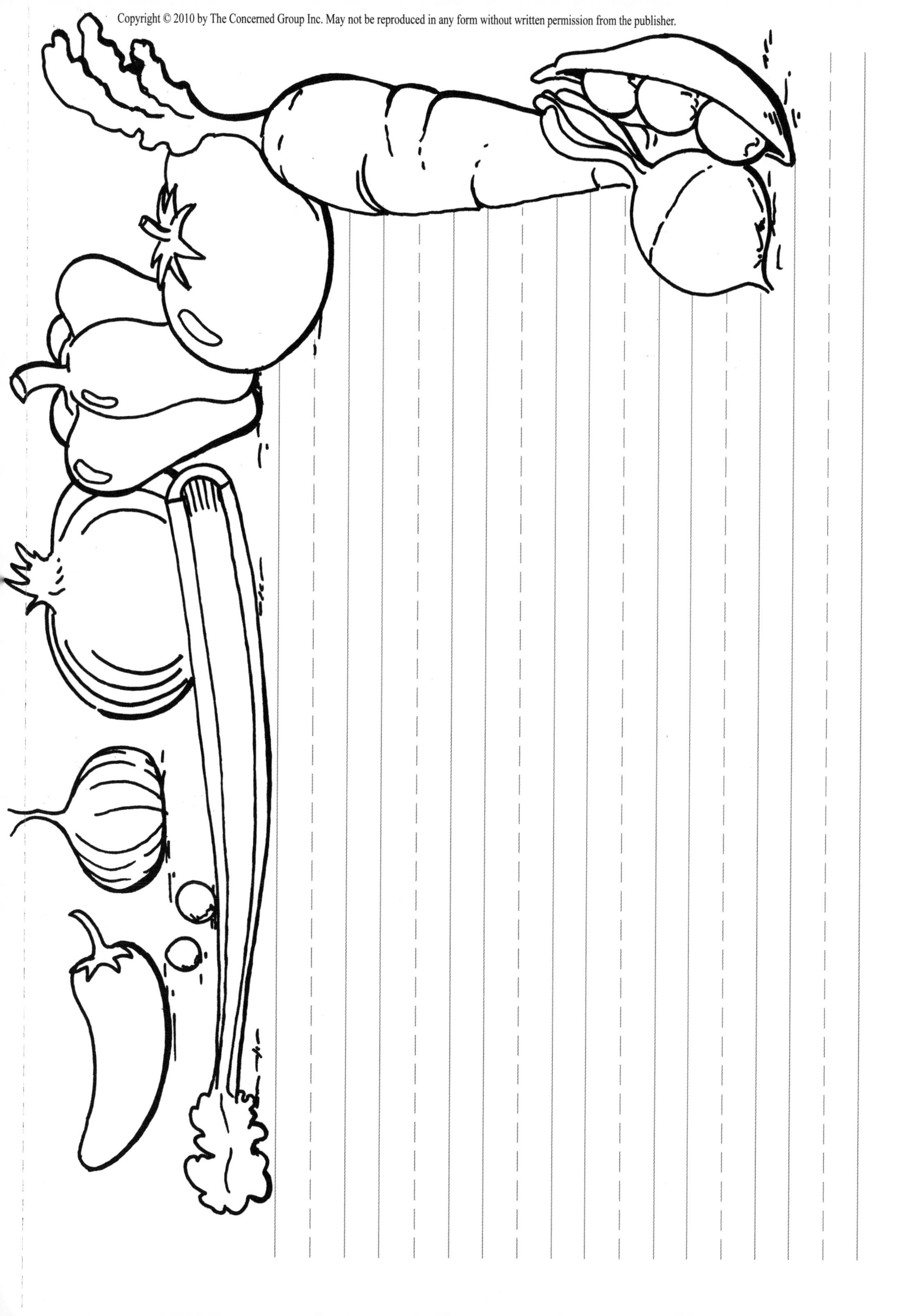

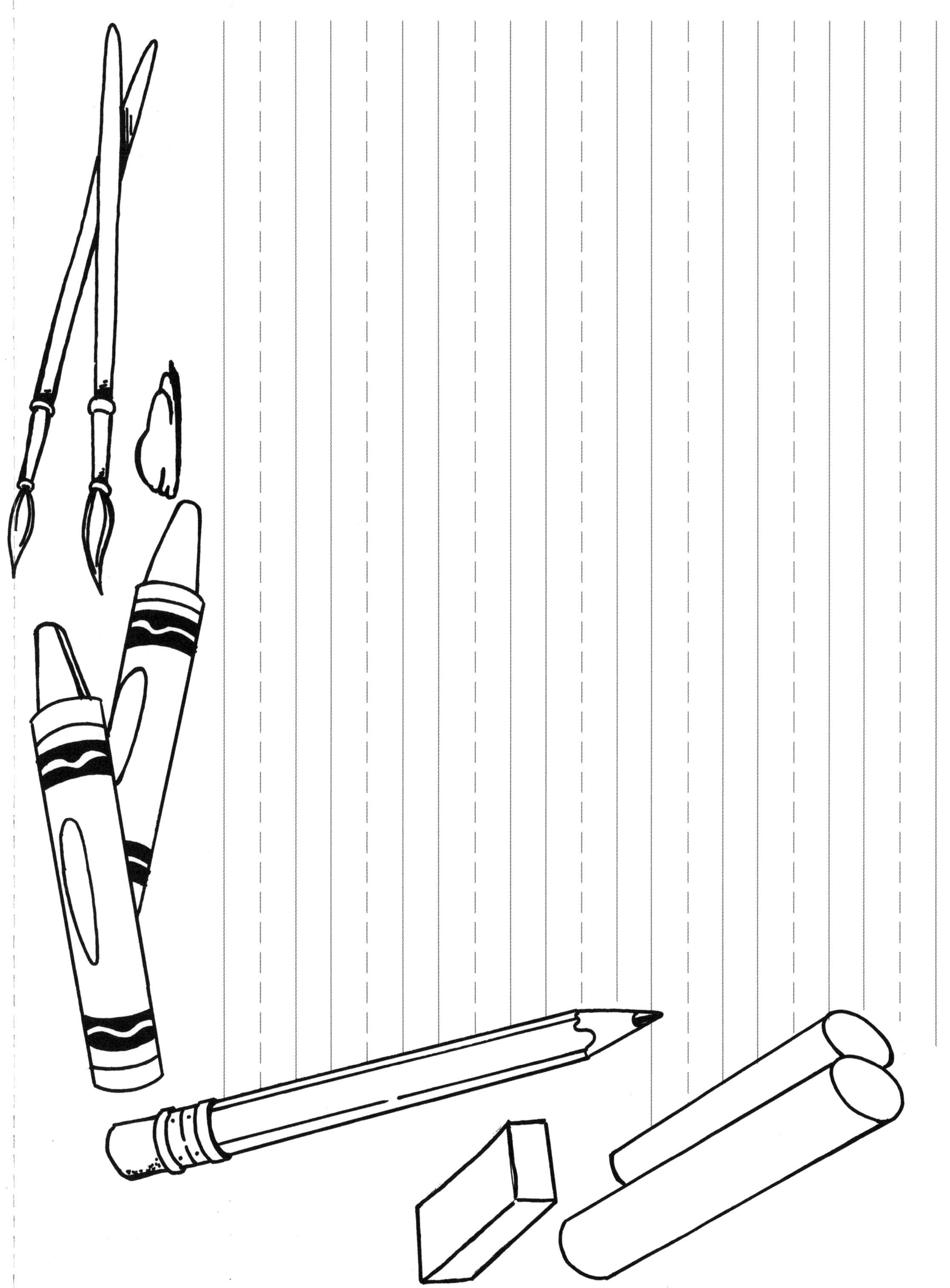

71422239R00037

Made in the USA
Columbia, SC
29 May 2017